PTUI!

**HERE COMES**

# SNOOPY

*Selected Cartoons From*

## SNOOPY Vol. I

by Charles M. Schulz

A FAWCETT CREST BOOK
FAWCETT PUBLICATIONS, INC., GREENWICH, CONN.
MEMBER OF AMERICAN BOOK PUBLISHERS COUNCIL, INC.

HERE COMES SNOOPY

This book, prepared especially for Fawcett Publications, Inc., comprises the first half of SNOOPY, and is reprinted by arrangement with Holt, Rinehart and Winston, Inc.

Twenty-first Fawcett Crest printing, May 1970

Published by Fawcett World Library,
67 West 44th Street, New York, N. Y. 10036
PRINTED IN THE UNITED STATES OF AMERICA

SCHULZ

SCHULZ

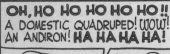

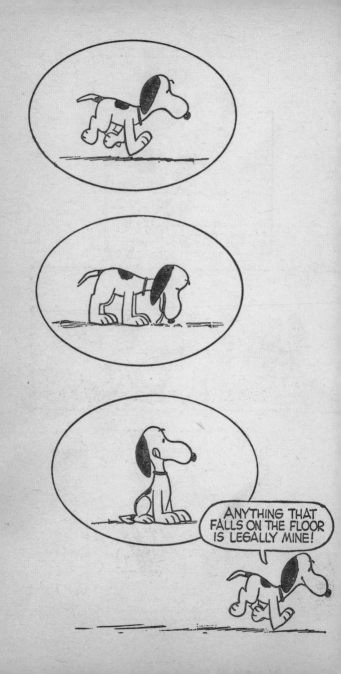

ZOOM!

NOW, YOU CUT THAT OUT!

SCHULZ

## KLUNK! BUMP!BUMP! bumpety-bump CRASH!!

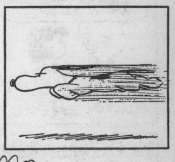

**ZIP!**

PHOOEY! I DIDN'T MIND NOT GETTING ANY CANDY, BUT I DIDN'T LIKE THAT REMARK, 'KINDLY REMOVE YOUR HAIRY FACE!'

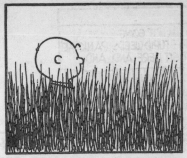

I THOUGHT I TOLD YOU TO STOP THAT DANCING?! YOU HAVE NO RIGHT TO BE SO HAPPY!!! NOW, STOP IT! DO YOU HEAR ME?!

SCHULZ

THERE SURE ARE A LOT OF WORMS ON THE SIDEWALK AFTER IT RAINS..

SCHULZ